COWBOY
WITHOUT A HORSE

By
Mary Jane Simonson

Illustrations
Ernest Lisle Reedstrom

BENEFIC PRESS
Westchester, Illinois

Cowboys of Many Races

Adam Bradford, Cowboy

Cowboy Without A Horse

Cowboy On The Mountain

Cowboy On The Trail

Editor,

Joellen Reiter

Library of Congress
Number 75-87129

Contents

1 Ride, Cowboys! Ride!

Ya-hoo!
Round up is here!
Ride, Cowboys! Ride!
Ride away to the big,
big land.

The cowboys round up cattle.
They ride and ride to find
the cattle on this big,
big land.

The cowboys like the
round up.
They like to ride and ride.
They like the big,
big land.

This is the cook.

He comes on the round up
to cook for the cowboys.

The cowboys like what
he cooks.

This is Bill.

Bill comes on the round up
with the cook.

Bill is a good cook, too.

But this is not what
Bill wants.

Bill wants to be a cowboy.

He wants to have a horse
like a cowboy.

And he wants to ride like
a cowboy.

2 The Cowboys Stop

The cowboys ride on and on.
But they can not find
the cattle.

"We will stop,"
said a cowboy.

"We will stop, and we will
look for the cattle in
the morning."

Bill and the cook
stop, too.

3 Wild Horses

Where will the cowboys find
the cattle?
They look and look
and ride and ride.

Look!
What is this the
cowboys see?
It is not cattle they see.
They see horses!
The horses run and jump
and play.

The cowboys can not
round up the horses.
The horses are wild.

Bill sees the wild
horses, too.
He sees the horse he wants.
But the wild horses
run away.

Can Bill find the wild
horse he wants?
    Can he ride the wild horse?
Can he be a cowboy?

"I will find the wild horse,"
said Bill.

"I will find the horse, and
he will be my horse.

"I will be a cowboy."

4 A Horse For Bill

Here they are!
Here are the wild horses.
Bill sees a horse run away.

This is the horse
Bill wants.
Bill runs, too.

Ya-hoo!
Bill did it!
The wild horse comes
to Bill.

Bill wants the horse to be
a cowboy's horse.
He wants a horse he can ride.
But a wild horse is wild.
A wild horse wants to play.

Bill said to the wild horse,
"You are Leader.

"I will teach you to be
a cowboy's horse.

"You will not be wild."

Bill is a
good teacher.
He teaches Leader
to run like a
cowboy's horse.

He teaches Leader
to jump like a
cowboy's horse.

He teaches Leader
to play like a
cowboy's horse.

Leader is a good horse.
Bill rides Leader around
and around on this big,
big land.

5 Proud Bill

Bill rides Leader to a
round up.
What a good ride
they have.

The cowboys see Leader.
"What a horse!" they said.
"What a good horse!"

Bill is proud.

A cowboy said to Bill,
"The cowboys and I have to
ride away to look for
lost cattle.

"Bill, you and Leader will
be here with the cattle
we have rounded up."

Bill likes this.
The cowboys are going
away, and he will be with
the cattle.

6 The Stampede

What is this?
What is going on?
The cattle run and jump.
They run and jump like
wild horses.

The cattle run away.
They will not stop.
It is a stampede.

Bill jumps up.
He will ride Leader.
He and Leader will have to
stop the stampede.

"Run, Leader! Run!"
said Bill.

"The cattle are going to
the canyon.

"They will go down in the
canyon and be lost.

"We will have to stop
the cattle."

Bill and Leader run to
stop the cattle.
But the cattle will
not stop.

Bill rides up and down.

Will Bill and Leader go down in the canyon?

Will the cattle go down in the canyon, too?

The cattle stop.
They will not go down in the canyon.
They will not be lost.

7 Cowboy Bill

"You stopped the stampede,"
a cowboy said to Bill.
"Good for you."

"I did not stop the
stampede," Bill said.
"Leader did.
"Leader is my horse, and
he can run like a wild horse."

"Good for Leader, too,"
said the cowboy.

And he said, "Bill, I want
you to be a cowboy for me.

"You will not cook.

"You will ride."

"Ya-hoo!" Bill said.
"I will be a cowboy!
"This is what I want, and
this is what Leader wants."

Leader runs and jumps like a wild horse.

A horse can be proud, too!

Vocabulary

The words used in this book should be familiar to pupils reading on the pre-primer level. For those pupils reading at this level, special emphasis should be placed on the words below. The number indicates the page on which the word first appears.

be 10	morning 12
but 10	
	proud 29
canyon 35	
cattle 6	ride 5
cook 8	round 5
cowboys 5	
	stampede 33
horse 10	stop 11
going 31	teach 24
land 5	wild 14
lost 30	

The Way To Say It

Make the sound of the letter r̲. Six words on page 5 begin with this sound. Can you find these words?

Another word on page 5 is made up of two words. What is it?

Some words are like each other because they rhyme. You can use words that rhyme to make up a poem. Some words from the story rhyme. They can be used to make up a poem about Bill.

> "I'll be a cowboy, I will.
> "I'll have a horse," said Bill.
> Now Bill is a cowboy—Ya-hoo!
> And he has a horse, Leader, too.

Make up your own poem about Bill.

You And They

The cowboy, Bill, lived on a ranch. Tell a story about Bill's home. Tell a story about your home. How are they alike? How are they different?

Things To Know

Read this and tell the things Bill needed to know to catch Leader.

One day Bill saw some wild horses. He wanted one of the horses. He wanted to ride this horse. But the wild horse ran away.

Bill went to look for the horse. He walked a long, long way. He looked at the ground. He looked near water. He listened. Then he saw the horse!

Bill had a rope, and he threw it over the horse's head. He pulled on the rope and brought the horse close to him. Bill touched the horse's nose. He gave him some sugar and named him Leader.

Would you like to know some of the things Bill knew? What things would they be? How would you use them?

How To Do It

Bill had to teach Leader not to be wild. On the next page are some of the things he taught Leader. Copy the lines on a piece of paper and write in the missing words from the word list on page 47.

46

Bill taught Leader to XXXX.
Bill taught Leader to XXX.
Bill taught Leader to XXXX.

play   run   jump

Would you like to teach a horse not to be wild? What would you need to learn to do it?

You Can Do It

In the story, Bill cooked for the cowboys on the round up. The food Bill cooked was carried in a special wagon called a chuck wagon. You can make a chuck wagon of your very own. Cut down the sides of a strong cardboard box and make four holes in each side as shown. Then cut four circles of the same size from heavy cardboard. Attach the wheels

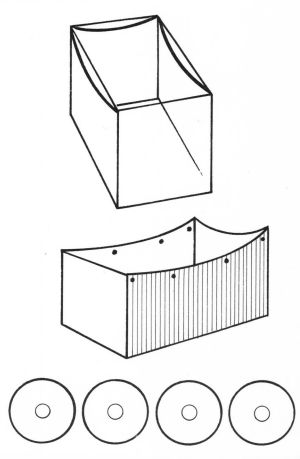

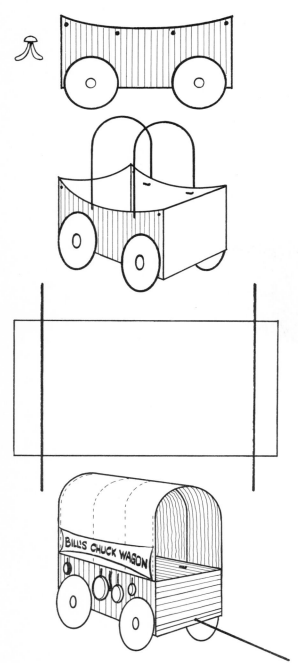

to the box with two-pronged paper fasteners. Bend two pipe cleaners and put them into the two middle holes in the sides of the box. This makes a frame for the top of the wagon. Cut a piece of heavy paper two inches longer than the box and wide enough to fit over the pipe cleaner frame. This will be the top of the wagon. With tape, fasten a pipe cleaner to each end of the top. Stretch the paper over the frame and thread the pipe cleaners through the holes at each end of the box. Fasten tightly. Now put a pipe cleaner into the centerfront of the box. And there you have your chuck wagon!

BILL'S CHUCK WAGON